Wales
SPY IT! SCORE IT!

Introduction

Wales sits to the west of central England in the UK. From its moody mountains to its beautiful beaches, its countryside does not disappoint. It also has plentiful culture, in the form of historic castles, palaces and cathedrals.

Welsh wildlife is not to be missed... from puffins to pine martens and red kites to red squirrels, you're sure to spot something fantastic.

And you'll never be bored in Wales either... why not have a go at surfing or coasteering on the Welsh coast, or take a train up to the top of Wales' highest mountain – Snowdon? Better still, see if you can climb it on foot (be sure to take a grown-up)!

Wherever you find yourself in Wales, and whatever you're up to, always keep your eyes peeled for the Welsh spots in this book!

How to use your i-SPY book

Keep your eyes peeled for the i-SPYs in the book.

If you spy it, score it by ticking the circle or star.

Items with a star are difficult to spot so you'll have to search high and low to find them.

Once you score 1000 points, send away for your super i-SPY certificate. Follow the instructions on page 64 to find out how.

50 POINTS

Cardiff

Cardiff has been the capital of Wales since 1955 (before then the capital had been Strata Florida Abbey and then Machynlleth), but there has been a settlement here since Roman times. It's a fascinating mix of old and new, with an incredibly modern waterfront along the Severn Estuary. Score for visiting Cardiff.

5 POINTS

National Museum Cardiff

This vast museum covers the history of Wales and is home to a Jurassic-era dinosaur fossil that was found in nearby Penarth. The art on display here is considered to be some of the best in Europe.

5 POINTS

Wales Millennium Centre

This striking modern building on Cardiff Bay opened in 2004. It's home to important performance companies such as the Welsh National Opera and the National Dance Company.

5 POINTS

Sir Gareth Edwards statue

In St David's shopping centre in Cardiff, you'll find a statue of the famous Welsh rugby player, Sir Gareth Edwards.

15 POINTS

City Hall

This grand building dates back to 1905 and its interior is even more ornate. Look for the dragon that sits on top of its central dome.

10 POINTS

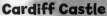

Cardiff Castle

Cardiff's castle is at the heart of the city. The 12-sided keep sits on top of a small hill and was built in Norman times, while parts of the residential buildings date back to the 16th century.

5 POINTS

Cardiff Bay

Cardiff's docks were once one of the busiest in the world but they became neglected after World War II. Since the late 1980s, the bay has been regenerated and is now full of interesting modern buildings, restaurants and shops.

5 POINTS

Cities - Cardiff

Roald Dahl Plass

This big plaza sits at the heart of Cardiff Bay and is named after the children's author, who was born in the city. Events and activities are often held here, such as a huge sandpit in the summer months.

5 POINTS

The Senedd

Another striking modern building on Cardiff Bay, the Senedd is home to the Welsh Parliament. It's possible to watch MPs discussing issues in the Debating Chamber.

5 POINTS

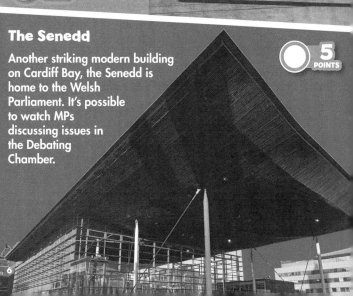

Swansea

Wales' second city has a lovely position on Swansea Bay, overlooking the Bristol Channel. During the Industrial Revolution this was an important centre for copper smelting. Score for visiting Swansea.

Swansea Museum

Created in 1841, this is the oldest museum in Wales. Highlights include an Egyptian mummy and a photo of Winston Churchill visiting the city during World War II.

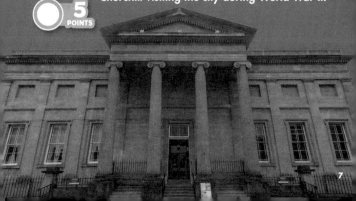

Cities – Swansea

National Waterfront Museum

There are 15 galleries in this hands-on museum which covers Welsh history and industry. You can have a look at a coal wagon or listen to music from some of Wales' most successful musicians.

10 POINTS

Swansea Bay

The city's position on Swansea Bay means there is an abundance of beaches on its doorstep. At the tip of the bay is The Mumbles, which has been a popular local seaside destination since the early 19th century.

5 POINTS

Dylan Thomas statue

A Welsh poet and writer, Dylan Thomas was born in Swansea. This bronze statue of him sits outside the Dylan Thomas Centre.

10 POINTS

Sail Bridge

Constructed in 2003, this striking bridge over the River Tawe definitely lives up to its name. It's sturdier than it looks as it has been designed to withstand the high winds that often affect this part of the city.

10 POINTS

Newport

This city grew up around its docks on the River Usk. There has been a port here since medieval times. Score for visiting Newport.

10 POINTS

St Woolos Cathedral

The origins of this cathedral date back to the 5th century, but there have been many changes and additions since then. Look out for some beautiful modern stained-glass windows.

15 POINTS

Newport Transporter Bridge

15 POINTS

This massive bridge is actually more like an aerial ferry: cars are carried on a kind of gondola from one side to the other. It's also possible to walk across it, but you'll need a head for heights.

This Little Piggy statue

10 POINTS

This statue of a life-size Gloucester Old Spot pig celebrates Newport's history as a market town. You'll find it outside the entrance to Newport market.

Tredegar House

Just outside of the city is this red-brick house, built in 1674 for the Morgan family. Three beautiful walled gardens surround the house.

20 POINTS

St Davids

St Davids has only been a city since 1995 and it still feels more like a large village. It sits at the westernmost point of Wales and is concentrated around its beautiful cathedral. Score for visiting St Davids.

10 POINTS

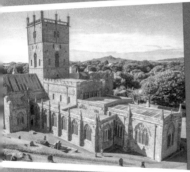

St Davids Cathedral

Wales' patron saint, St David, was born and buried here and it has been an important pilgrimage site for 1500 years. Building started here in 1181, though the beautiful tower dates from the 13th century.

10 POINTS

St Davids Bishop's Palace

The ruins of this beautiful palace date back to the 13th and 14th centuries. Look out for the carved human heads, animals and mythological creatures on the arches.

15 POINTS

12

Bangor

This small city in North Wales is largely Welsh speaking. Its university dates back to the late 19th century and looks down over the town. Score for visiting Bangor.

15 POINTS

Bangor Cathedral

This cathedral started life as a monastic cell back in 530, making it one of the oldest Christian sites in Britain. Much of what can be seen today is the result of work by the Victorian architect Sir George Gilbert Scott.

15 POINTS

Garth Pier

The second-longest pier in Wales, Garth Pier stretches out across the Menai Strait towards the Isle of Anglesey. Opened in 1896, its length is dotted with little ornate kiosks.

15 POINTS

Penrhyn Castle

Though this castle looks like it might be Norman, it's actually from the Victorian period. It sits just outside of the city and has beautiful grounds to explore.

20 POINTS

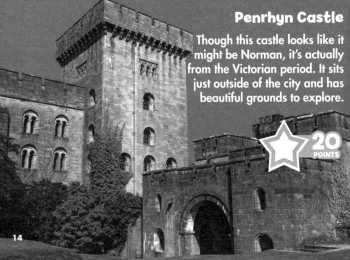

Countryside

Snowdonia National Park

Home to the highest mountain in Wales (Snowdon – see p.50), this national park covers a vast stretch of northwest Wales. Among the mountain peaks are peaceful lakes, wild waterfalls and lots of farmland.

10 POINTS

Mountain biker

With a number of big cycling routes crossing the country, Wales is considered one of the best cycling destinations in Britain. There are over 1,900 kilometres of cycle network paths in Wales.

5 POINTS

Countryside

Stone circle

There are many stone circles and standing stones in Wales, which date back to prehistoric times. Look out too for ancient burial chambers, which are even older than the stone circles.

20 POINTS

Hiker

Wales' wild scenery makes it a popular destination for hikers, whether it's along the coastal paths or into the mountains. There are also lots of options for more gentle short walks.

5 POINTS
Score double for doing a hike.

Wye Valley

Sitting on the border with England, this lush valley only became part of Wales in 1974. It stretches from the border town of Chepstow in the south to Monmouth in the north.

10 POINTS

Waterfall

Wales has lots of beautiful waterfalls, undoubtedly as a result of the high rainfall in Wales. The country's biggest waterfall is Pistyll Rhaeadr, in northern Powys.

5 POINTS

Brecon Beacons National Park

This national park in south Wales is named after the mountains that stretch across its middle. It's also an International Dark Sky Reserve, which means that it's brilliant for stargazing.

10 POINTS

Countryside

Farmland

A large proportion of the Welsh countryside is used for farming, especially grazing animals. Wales is particularly well known for sheep farming.

5 POINTS

River

Wales is crisscrossed by countless rivers – look out for the word 'afon', which is Welsh for river.

5 POINTS

Rock climbing

Rock climbing is a popular activity in Wales, with Snowdon offering some of the best opportunities, even for beginners. Look out too for people climbing sea cliffs in places like Pembrokeshire.

15 POINTS

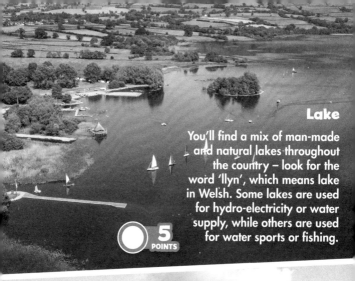

Lake

You'll find a mix of man-made and natural lakes throughout the country – look for the word 'llyn', which means lake in Welsh. Some lakes are used for hydro-electricity or water supply, while others are used for water sports or fishing.

5 POINTS

Valley

A valley is an area of low land, usually with a river, that sits between hills or mountains. Wales' many beautiful rivers pass through some lovely valleys, such as the lush Wye Valley in the easternmost part of the country.

10 POINTS

Black Mountains

Known in Welsh as Y Mynyddoedd Duon, the Black Mountains occupy the northernmost part of the Brecon Beacons National Park. The highest mountain here is Waun Fach, standing at 2,661 feet (811 metres).

20 POINTS

Whitewater rafting

There are a number of stretches of river here where whitewater rafting is possible. The beautiful Tryweryn River in north Wales is known for having excellent rafting conditions.

30 POINTS

Woodland

Woodland can be found throughout the country, though north Wales in particular is home to some amazing forests, which are at their best in autumn as the leaves change colour.

15 POINTS

Llyn Tegid

At 4 miles (6.4 km) long, Llyn Tegid (Bala Lake in English) is the biggest natural lake in Wales. The winds here make it a great spot for windsurfing.

10 POINTS

Countryside

Footpath signs

Footpath signs, which are often marked with yellow arrows, help guide you on your way when walking. There are a number of long-distance footpaths in Wales, such as Offa's Dyke Path, which have special signposts.

Mountain

The mountains of Wales were carved out during the Ice Age. In addition to Snowdon in north Wales, there's also the Cambrian Mountains in mid Wales and the Black Mountains in the Brecon Beacons.

10 POINTS

Castle

There are over 400 castles in Wales, ranging from Norman ruins to ornate Victorian palaces. Most have a defensive river or coastal position.

Canal

There are four canals in Wales: Llangollen, Montgomery, Swansea, and Monmouthshire & Brecon. They were originally built during the Industrial Revolution to help transport materials such as lime, iron and slate.

Coast

Pembrokeshire Coast National Park

The only coastal national park in Britain is home to some of the loveliest stretches of golden sand in Wales. One of the best ways to explore the cliffs and beaches is to walk part or all of the Pembrokeshire Coast Path.

10 POINTS

Surfer

Wales has a number of excellent surfing beaches, including Whitesands Bay in Pembrokeshire and Llangennith on the Gower Peninsular. A wetsuit is essential for coping with the cold water.

15 POINTS

Double points if you try surfing.

Aberystwyth

Often called just 'Aber', Aberystwyth sits in a fantastic position on the Cambrian coast. Marine Terrace, which overlooks North Beach, has lots of colourful old houses.

 10 POINTS

Coasteering

Coasteering was invented by surfers in Pembrokeshire in the 1980s and Wales remains one of the best places to see and join the activity. It involves a combination of hiking, cliff jumping, scrambling over rocks and swimming.

TOP SPOT!

 50 POINTS

25

Coast

Gower Peninsula

The Gower Peninsular juts out into the Bristol Channel to the southwest of Swansea. As well as lovely beaches and dramatic cliffs, there's also ruined castles and sweet villages to explore.

10 POINTS

Fishing boat

Wales' coastline has meant that fishing has been an important industry for the country. Look out for fishing boats, especially in small seaside towns, which might range from small, colourful ones to much larger trawlers.

5 POINTS

Ferry

Ferries run from Ireland to three ferry ports in Wales: Holyhead, Fishguard and Pembroke Dock.

20 POINTS

Llŷn Peninsula

30 POINTS

The most westerly point of Wales, the beaches of the Llŷn face the Irish Sea. It's a lot less developed than other stretches of coast and has lots of old fishing villages.

Cliff

There are cliffs all along Wales' coastline, carved out by the wind, rain and sea over thousands and thousands of years. The towering cliffs at Marloes Sands in Pembrokeshire are particularly rugged.

5 POINTS

Sea kayaking

Sea kayaking is a great way to explore Wales' beautiful coast and you'll often see people on the water in these small paddle boats. The waters around Anglesey and the Llŷn Peninsula are particularly popular with kayakers.

20 POINTS

Aberaeron

This small town on Cardigan Bay, in west Wales, has brightly coloured 19th-century buildings overlooking its harbour.

20 POINTS

Coast path

There are a number of established footpaths in Wales that follow the coastline – all together, they stretch for 870 miles (1,400 km) and make up the impressive Wales Coast Path. It's possible to do everything from short rambles to multi-day hikes.

5 POINTS

Coast

Rock pool

There are some great opportunities for rock pooling when the tide goes. Look out for hermit crabs, common starfish and sea anemones.

10 POINTS

Sandy beach

5 POINTS

Wales has miles and miles of sandy beaches, from tucked-away coves to wide stretches of golden sand that are perfect for buckets and spades.

Colourful seaside houses

In some of Wales' seaside towns you'll find houses painted in bright colours, often around the harbour or seafront. Tenby and Aberaeron are particularly well known for this.

10 POINTS

Pebble beach

The stones on pebble beaches have been worn down by the sea over thousands and thousands of years. They're great places to try your hand at stone skimming.

10 POINTS

Lifeboat

There are around 30 lifeboat stations in Wales, including at New Quay, Holyhead and Aberystwyth. It's often possible to see the boats inside their sheds when they're not in action, but look out for them too when they're out on the water.

30 POINTS

Llandudno

Llandudno, on the north coast, was developed as a seaside resort by the Victorians. It's home to the longest pier in Wales, which is almost half a mile (700 m) in length.

Lighthouse

Wales is home to over 30 lighthouses, though not all of them still operate. Lighthouses do a vital job protecting ships and boats by warning them of land nearby.

Islands

Isle of Anglesey

Known as Ynys Môn in Welsh, Anglesey is Wales' biggest island. As well as many gorgeous beaches, the island is home to a large number of ancient sites. Score for visiting Anglesey.

15 POINTS

Britannia Bridge

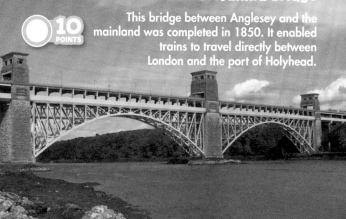

10 POINTS

This bridge between Anglesey and the mainland was completed in 1850. It enabled trains to travel directly between London and the port of Holyhead.

Holy Island

The port of Holyhead, from which ferries depart for Ireland, is on this small island off the west coast of Anglesey, to which it's connected by a short bridge.

20 POINTS

30 POINTS

Llanddwyn Island

Off the southwest coast of Anglesey, this island is actually attached to the mainland – except at high tide. When the tide is low, you can walk out here from Newborough Warran to see the lighthouse and the ruined church.

South Stack

The main reason to visit this small island is for its seabirds, which include puffins and guillemots. It's reached by a suspension bridge from Holy Island.

Skomer

Skomer Island lies off the Pembrokeshire coast. It's particularly famous for its puffin population, which is best seen from May to July.

Islands

Skokholm

Two miles south of Skomer, Skokholm is also known for its birdlife. Britain's first bird observatory was founded here in the 1930s.

30 POINTS

Grassholm

It's not possible to land on this small island off the Pembrokeshire coast, but you can see its most famous sight from a boat: gannets. The island has a huge colony of these seabirds.

50 POINTS

TOP SPOT!

Boat trip

One of the best ways to see some of Wales' islands is on a boat trip. You might even be able to see wildlife like puffins, seals and dolphins. Score for seeing a boat trip.

10 POINTS

Score double if you go on a boat trip.

Ramsey Island

20 POINTS

This island, which is looked after by the Royal Society for the Protection of Birds (RSPB), sits about a kilometre away from St Davids. Nesting puffins and shearwaters can be seen here in spring, while seal pups make an appearance in the autumn months. Score for spotting or visiting Ramsey Island.

37

Wildlife

Puffin

There are a few puffin populations in Wales, and one of the best places to see these brightly-billed seabirds is on a boat trip to Skomer Island (see p.35).

30 POINTS

Red kite

Red kites can often be seen soaring over woods and fields in Wales. Look for their russet colours and distinctive, forked tails.

10 POINTS

Seal

Two species of seals can be found in Wales: grey and harbour or common. Pembrokeshire is the best place to catch a sighting – look for fluffy grey seal pups (like the pup here) in the autumn months.

10 POINTS

Dolphin

Cardigan Bay is home to the biggest resident population of dolphins in Britain. Summer is the best time to see them, particularly on a boat trip out from New Quay.

20 POINTS

Osprey

The rarest bird in Wales. The best place to try to see one is at the Brenig Osprey Project in North Wales, where they can usually be spotted from April to August.

TOP SPOT!

50 POINTS

Manx shearwater

With black tops and white bellies, these noisy birds nest on Wales' offshore islands from March to April. Skomer Island is one of the best places to see them.

20 POINTS

10 POINTS

Dragonfly

There are 37 species of dragonflies in the country, ranging from the common clubtail to blue-tailed damselflies. Look out for them along rivers and streams.

Black grouse

These endangered birds can be found in mid and north Wales. While the males are black with bright red patches above their eyes, females have reddish-brown feathers that help to camouflage them during the nesting season.

50 POINTS

TOP SPOT!

Lapwing

Often found on farmland and wetland, lapwings can usually be identified by the long black crests on their heads. Look out for them taking to the sky in huge numbers in winter.

20 POINTS

Welsh mountain sheep

Wales is famous for having lots of sheep. True to their name, you'll find Welsh mountain sheep at higher altitudes. Their fleece is long and thick to keep them warm in the hills, and the males often have curved horns.

5 POINTS

41

Red squirrel

Red squirrels are one of the country's rarest mammals. The best places to see them are in and around Anglesey, such as in the grounds of Plas Newydd, close to the Menai Strait.

 40 POINTS

Pine marten

Pine martens were once one of the most common woodland creatures in Britain, but sightings are now very rare. Look for them in forests in mid Wales.

 40 POINTS

Polecat

Part of the weasal family, polecats are found all over Wales. They are mainly nocturnal, though you might have a better chance of seeing them in daylight during the summer months when females hunt for food for their babies.

Slow worm

It's easy to mistake these legless lizards for small snakes, especially with their long, shiny bodies. They are either grey or brown, but are quite harmless and are usually found in meadows and woodlands.

Food

Laverbread

Despite the name, this isn't a kind of bread. This Welsh delicacy is made from laver seaweed, which is boiled and then pureed or minced. It's often eaten as part of a Welsh breakfast.

20 POINTS

Caerphilly cheese

This is a hard white cheese that originated in the town of Caerphilly, in south Wales. It's traditionally used to make Welsh rarebit.

5 POINTS

Welsh cake

These little griddle cakes are a bit like flattened scones and are made with currants and spices like cinnamon and nutmeg. They're usually lightly dusted with sugar.

5 POINTS

Glamorgan sausage

These vegetarian sausages are usually made with Caerphilly cheese, leeks and eggs, before being rolled in breadcrumbs and fried.

15 POINTS

Bara brith

The name bara brith translates from Welsh to English as 'speckled bread'. This is a traditional tea bread, made with dried fruit, tea and spices.

5 POINTS

Anglesey eggs

This traditional dish, called Ŵyau Ynys Môn in Welsh, is made from mashed potatoes, leeks and hard-boiled eggs, which are baked in a cheese sauce. As the name suggests, it originated on the Isle of Anglesey.

30 POINTS

Food

Crempogau

Welsh pancakes are a little like American pancakes in their size. They're sometimes served in a stack with butter, and are usually eaten on Shrove Tuesday.

20 POINTS

Welsh rarebit

Originally called 'Welsh rabbit', despite containing no meat, this is a kind of cheese on toast, often made with Caerphilly as well as mustard, Worcestershire sauce and beer.

5 POINTS

Conwy mussels

The fishing village of Conwy in north Wales is home to these delicious mussels. Conwy is located on an estuary where the River Conwy meets the Irish Sea, and the combination of freshwater and seawater is said to make these mussels the tastiest around!

10 POINTS

Lamb

Unsurprisingly for a country with a lot of sheep farming, lamb is a popular ingredient in Wales. You'll likely see it served roasted or in soups and stews.

 5 POINTS

Leek

This root vegetable grows really well in the Welsh climate, and you'll often see them included in various dishes on restaurant menus. They're also the national symbol of Wales, so look out for them in soldier's caps on St David's Day (1st March).

 5 POINTS

Cawl

The word cawl can be used to describe any soup or broth, but the most traditional recipe includes chunks of mutton, leeks, potatoes, swedes and carrots.

5 POINTS

Famous landmarks

Portmeirion 10 POINTS

This quirky village on Tremadog Bay in north Wales looks like a little slice of Italy. It was built between 1925 and 1973 and has been used in many films and TV series.

Hercules statue

In the centre of Portmeirion, you'll find a bronze statue of Hercules, Greek god and son of Zeus, carrying the weight of the world on his shoulders. 15 POINTS

Cadair Idris

There are many legends about this mountain in southern Snowdonia, often involving a giant called Idris. The hike to the top is considered by some walkers to be harder than that up Mount Snowdon.

 20 POINTS

Carreg Cennen Castle

10 POINTS

These castle ruins have a fantastic position above the Cennen River, with views across the valleys below. It was built in the 13th century and partially destroyed in the 15th century.

Mad Hatter statue

10 POINTS

Sculpted from half of a 9-tonne oak tree by Simon Hedger, this statue of the Mad Hatter character from Lewis Carroll's book *Alice's Adventures In Wonderland* can be found on the promenade in Llandudno.

Ffestiniog Railway

10 POINTS

This railway line was originally opened in 1836 to carry slate from the mines at Blaenau Ffestiniog to the port at Porthmadog. Today it is a big visitor attraction, with the steam train carrying people along the scenic 13½-mile (21.7-km) route to Snowdonia.

49

Famous landmarks

Mount Snowdon

At 3,560 feet (1,085 metres), Snowdon is the highest mountian in Wales. Snow can often be seen on the top as late as April. Climbing Snowdon is very popular, so it can get crowded in the summer months.

20 POINTS

Double points for climbing to the top.

Tintern Abbey

Set on the banks of the River Wye, this beautiful Gothic abbey was founded by monks in 1131. It was surrendered during Henry VIII's reign and fell in to ruin.

15 POINTS

Caerleon

Caerleon is believed by many to be the site of Camelot, the court of King Arthur. The remains you can see here today are from its time as an important Roman military station.

15 POINTS

20 POINTS

National Botanic Garden

These beautiful gardens in Camarthenshire are home to the world's largest single-span glasshouse, which houses endangered plants.

Famous landmarks

Powis Castle

This medieval castle lies just outside the town of Welshpool, close to the English border. It's one of the country's most famous fortresses, and is also known for its beautiful gardens.

20 POINTS

Centre for Alternative Technology

This eco centre in mid Wales was set up in 1974 and researches environmentally friendly ways of living.

40 POINTS

Devil's Bridge

Devil's Bridge is in fact three bridges built on top of each other. Legend has it that the Devil built the original bridge here, though it was actually thought to be built by monks in the 11th century.

30 POINTS

Pontcysyllte Aqueduct

Standing high above the River Dee in north Wales, this aqueduct stretches for an amazing 1,000 feet (305 m) as part of the Llangollen Canal. You can either walk or take a narrowboat across it.

20 POINTS

Famous landmarks

Conwy Castle

Towering over the lovely town of Conwy on Wales' north coast, this medieval castle is one of the finest in the country. Score for spotting the castle or taking a walk about its battlements.

10 POINTS

Pentre Ifan

A Neolithic burial tomb, this is the largest of its type in the country. The massive top stone weighs 16 tonnes.

30 POINTS

Caernarfon Castle

Edward I of England began this fortress as part of his Iron Ring of castles in the 13th century. The Iron Ring of castles was a set of castles built, on King Edward I's command, around northern Wales after the death of the last Prince of Wales. This was to control the Welsh population, who resisted the English crown for hundreds of years. Despite its age, Caernarfon Castle's exterior is still in great condition today.

10 POINTS

Famous landmarks

Smallest house in Great Britain

This tiny, bright red building in Conwy was lived in until 1900. It measures just 1.83 m wide and 3.1 m high.

30 POINTS

Culture and celebrations

Hay Festival

One of the world's most famous book festivals, this 10-day celebration takes place annually in May in the border town of Hay-on-Wye.

10 POINTS

Abergavenny Food Festival

This is Wales' biggest foodie event, held for a weekend every September. There's always lots of interesting talks and classes, plus plenty of food tastings.

20 POINTS

St David's Day

Wales' national day falls on 1 March and is celebrated across the country. Look out for parades and concerts, and children going to school in traditional dress.

30 POINTS

National Eisteddfod

This huge celebration of Welsh culture is the biggest event in the country, with literature and arts events, poetry competitions and Welsh-language lessons. It's held in a different location each year.

20 POINTS

Royal Welsh Show

Held in July, this is one of the largest agricultural shows in Europe and a great day out. Animals are judged and awarded prizes, there's lots of tasty farm food to try, and you can watch sheep-shearing and falconry displays.

20 POINTS

World Bog Snorkelling Championships

This unusual event takes place at Waen Rhydd bog in mid Wales every August bank holiday Sunday. People from around the world come to participate.

50 POINTS

TOP SPOT!

Tenby Arts Festival

This festival is held in September and has been running for over 30 years. It hosts all sorts of music, drama and art workshops and performances.

30 POINTS

Male voice choirs

Wales is known for its singing traditions, and particularly for its male voice choirs. Many of these choirs started during the coal-mining days, when coal mining was a huge part of the Welsh economy and many men were employed in this industry. Score for seeing a male voice choir perform, or for seeing concert posters.

25 POINTS

Iconic Wales

Mine

Coal mining played a huge role in the country's past, but only a handful of private mines remain today. Score for visiting mining attractions, such as the Big Pit National Coal Museum in Blaenafon.

50 POINTS

Llanfairpwllgwyngyllgogerychwyrndrobwll-llantysiliogogogoch

This village in north Wales is famous for having the longest place name in Europe. You'll also see its shorter version used: Llanfairpwll.

20 POINTS

Rugby

The Welsh are passionate about rugby, and you'll find it played across the country. The national team usually play in red tops and can sometimes be seen at the Principality Stadium in Cardiff.

10
POINTS

Welsh flag

The national flag of Wales consists of a red dragon, with his tongue sticking out, on a white and green background. Its first recorded use was in the 9th century.

5
POINTS

Iconic Wales

Daffodil

This yellow spring flower is the country's national flower and you'll see it being worn on St David's Day. Score for seeing real daffodils or anything decorated with a daffodil.

5 POINTS

Love spoon

These decorative wooden spoons date back to the 17th century, when they were given as a symbol of love. Today you'll often find them in gift shops.

10 POINTS

Welsh sign

Most signs in Wales will have both Welsh and English instructions and destination names.

5 POINTS

Mae gan feicwyr flaenoriaeth

Cyclists have priority

Index

i-SPY How to get your i-SPY certificate and badge

Let us know when you' ve become a super-spotter with 1000 points and we'll send you a special certificate and badge!

Here's what to do:

- Ask an adult to check your score.

- Apply for your certificate at
  www.collins.co.uk/i-SPY
  (if you are under the age of 13 we'll need a parent or guardian to do this).

- We'll email your certificate and post you a brilliant badge!